Be Quiet, Marina!

Thanks to the Bank Street Family Center
for nurturing Moira and Marina, along
with many other children. And also thanks
for letting us tell the story.

Be Quiet, Marina!

By Kirsten DeBear

Photographs by Laura Dwight

Star Bright Books
Cambridge, Massachusetts

Published in the United States of America by Star Bright Books, Inc.

The name Star Bright Books and the Star Bright Books logo are registered trademarks of Star Bright Books, Inc. Please visit www.starbrightbooks.com. For bulk orders, email: orders@starbrightbooks.com, or call customer service at: (617) 354-1300.

Hardback ISBN-13: 978-1-887734-79-0
Printed in China 9 8 7 6 5 4 3 2

Paperback ISBN-13: 879-1-59572-665-0
Star Bright Books / MA / 00108130
Printed in China / Jade / 10 9 8 7 6 5 4 3 2 1

Printed on paper from sustainable forests and a percentage of post-consumer paper.

Design by Design Press, a division of the Savannah College of Art and Design.

Library of Congress Cataloging-in-Publication Data

DeBear, Kirsten.
    Be quiet, Marina! / by Kirsten DeBear ; photographs by Laura Dwight.
        p. cm.
Summary: A noisy little girl with cerebral palsy and a quiet little girl with Down syndrome learn to play together and eventually become best friends.
    ISBN 1-887734-79-1
    [1. Friendship--Fiction. 2. Play--Fiction. 3. Cerebral palsy--Fiction.
4. Physically handicapped--Fiction. 5. Down syndrome--Fiction. 6. Mentally handicapped--Fiction.] I. Dwight, Laura, ill. II. Title.
    PZ7.D3526 Be 2001
    [E]--dc21

                                                                00-012235

For Moira and Marina and their families.

This is Marina.  This is Moira.

 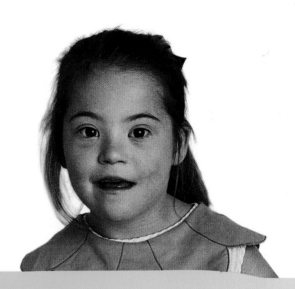

Marina and Moira go to the same school and are good friends.

In the beginning it was hard for them to play together. This story will tell you why that was so, and how they became good friends.

In many ways Marina and Moira were the same.
Marina was four years old.
Moira was also four years old.

They both liked to dance.

They both liked to
play ball.

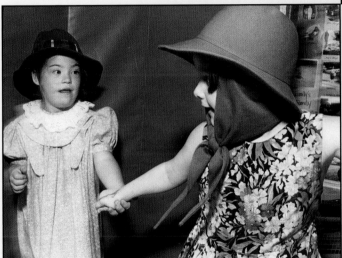

They both liked to
dress up.

And they both liked
to play with dolls.

In other ways they were different.
Marina had short hair. Moira had long hair.

Marina liked noise. She liked to scream and shout.

She liked to tell Moira what to do when they played together.

Moira did not like noise. She liked to sit quietly in her cubby.

And she liked to play with little people.

Marina liked to run ahead when the class went walking. Moira liked to stay with the teachers and other children.

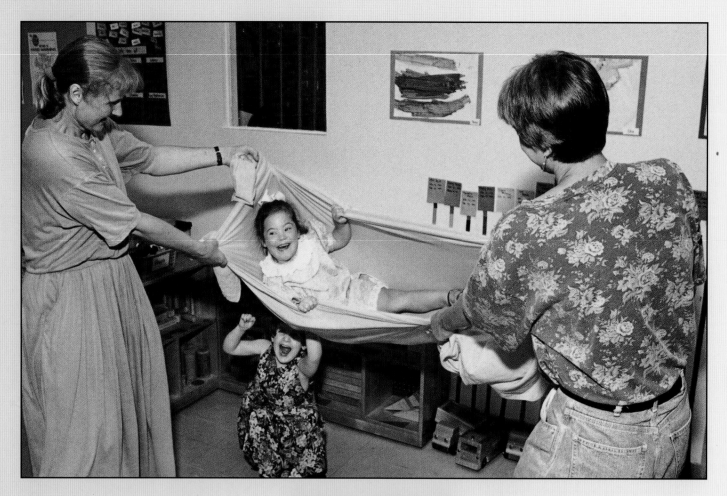

Sometimes the teachers swung the children in a blanket. Both Moira and Marina liked that.

But Marina did not like to wait for her turn. She got angry and screamed and cried.

That made
Moira feel
scared.

So she covered her
ears and went
away into the hall.

Both Marina and Moira liked to play with blocks.

When they finished they had to clean up. But Marina did not like to do that.

She got angry and screamed. Her screaming frightened Moira. So she covered her ears...

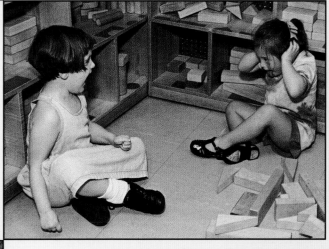

...and went away.

One day on the playground
Moira was on the see-saw.
Marina wanted to get on,
too. But she couldn't . . .

So she started
to scream.

She screamed so loudly
that Moira covered
her ears and walked
away.

Now Marina could get
on the see-saw, but it
was no fun alone.

Another day when Moira and Marina were playing telephones, Marina started to get upset.

This time something different happened. Moira did not run away. Instead she said,

"Please don't scream!"

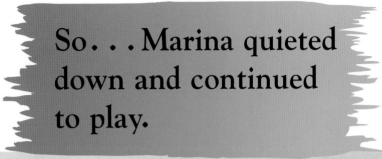

So . . . Marina quieted down and continued to play.

Another day, when Marina asked Moira, "Can I play with you?" Moira said,

"Yes, but don't scream!"

"O.K.," said Marina, "I won't."

Then they played birthday party and dolls together.

Moira used to be scared of Marina. But now she knows that Marina is her friend and she can tell her not to scream. And Marina knows that if she wants to play with Moira she must not scream.

And they also know that they can
ask their teacher to help them.

Now Marina and Moira are good friends.

Marina and Moira love to play on the see-saw together. It balances and they go up and down together.

"It's fun!" screams Marina.

Moira almost lets go of the handle to cover her ears, but instead she shouts:

Be Quiet, Marina!

In many ways Marina and Moira are just like other children. Some children are loud like Marina, while others prefer quiet like Moira.

But in some ways, Marina and Moira are different from other children because of their disabilities.

Marina was born with cerebral palsy. She cannot make her right hand do what she wants. This makes it impossible for her to play with things for which she needs two hands. Her left leg is also a problem. It is hard for her to lift it or balance on it. She has to wear a brace, or 'Orthotics,' inside her shoe to help her walk. She needs help to learn to balance and to use her left hand instead of her right.

It is hard for Marina to take it easy. She would like to move fast and do what she wants to do without help. She gets confused and angry when her body won't do what she wants it to do.

Moira has Down syndrome. People with Down syndrome have similar facial features. Like all people with Down syndrome, Moira's fingers are shorter than those of most children her age, and she needs extra help to learn to do some things that other children find easy. It is hard for her to jump and to learn to ride a tricycle.

Marina and Moira may look and act differently because of their disabilities, but their feelings are the same as everyone else's. All of us sometimes feel that there is too much noise and we want to run away, like Moira. And all of us have times when we feel frustrated and want to scream, like Marina. We all have to learn to live in a world full of noise and commotion, and we all have to learn to tolerate frustration. Moira and Marina teach us that in spite of difficulties and differences, we can all get along.

Resources

UNITED STATES

Council for Exceptional Children
2900 Crystal Drive, Suite 1000
Arlington, VA 22202-3557
Phone: (888) 232-7733
TTY: (866) 915-5000
e-mail: service@cec.sped.org
http://www.cec.sped.org

National Down Syndrome Congress
30 Mansell Court, Suite 108
Roswell, GA 30076
Phone: (800) 232-6372 (NDSC)
(770) 604-9500
mail: info@ndsccenter.org
http://www.ndsccenter.org

National Down Syndrome Society
666 Broadway, 8th Floor
New York, NY 10012
Phone: (800) 221-4602
(212) 460-9330
e-mail: info@ndss.org
http://www.ndss.org

National Dissemination Center for Children with Disabilities
(NICHCY)
1825 Connecticut Ave. NW
Washington, DC 20009
Phone: (800) 695-0285 (Voice/TTY)
(202) 884-8200 (Voice/TTY)
e-mail: nichcy@fhi360.org
http://www.nichcy.org

United Cerebral Palsy
1825 K Street NW, Suite 600
Washington, DC 20006
Phone: (800) 872-5827
(202) 776-0406
e-mail: info@ucp.org
http://www.ucp.org

CANADA

Canadian Down Syndrome Society
Suite 103 - 2003 14th Street N.W.
Calgary, Alberta T2M 3N4
Phone: (800) 883-5608
(403) 270-8500
e-mail: info@cdss.ca
http://www.cdss.ca

Cerebral Palsy Association in Alberta
12001 44 Street SE
Calgary, Alberta T2Z 4G9
Phone: (800) 363-2807
(403) 543-1161
e-mail: admin@cpalberta.com
http://www.cpalberta.com

Ontario Federation for Cerebral Palsy
Suite 104 - 1630 Lawrence Avenue West
Toronto, Ontario M6L 1C5
Phone: (877) 244-9686
(416) 244-9686
TTY: (416) 246-9122
e-mail: info@ofcp.ca
http://www.ofcp.ca

UNITED KINGDOM

Down Syndrome Association
Langdon Down Centre
2a Langdon Park
Teddington Middlesex TW11 9PS
Phone: (0333) 1212-300
e-mail: info@downs-syndrome.org.uk
http://www.downs-syndrome.org.uk

SCOPE
6 Market Road
London N7 9PW
Phone: (0808) 800 3333
e-mail: response@scope.org.uk
http://www.scope.org.uk

AUSTRALIA

Cerebral Palsy Association of Western Australia
106 Bradford Street
Coolbinia WA 6050
Toll free: (1800) 198 263
Phone: (08) 9443 0211
e-mail: info@tccp.com.au
http://www.tccp.com.au/

Down Syndrome Association of New South Wales, Inc.
7 Deed Place
Northmead NSW 2152
Phone: (02) 9841 4444
e-mail: admin@dsansw.org.au
http://www.downsyndromensw.org.au

Down Syndrome Association of Victoria
219 Napier Street
Fitzroy VIC 3065
Toll free: (1300) 658-873
Phone: (03) 9486-9600
e-mail: info@dsav.asn.au
http://www.downsyndromevictoria.org.au

SOUTH AFRICA

Down Syndrome South Africa
2 Ernest Oppenheimer Street
Lakeside Two, Office 109
Bruma, Johannesburg
Phone: (0861) 369672 (DOWNSA)
http://www.downsyndrome.org.za/
dssaoffice@icon.co.za

Down Syndrome Association of Kwazulu/Natal
382 Stella Road
Malvern, Durban 4055
Phone: (031) 464 2055
downskzn@iafrica.com